The Return of
The Spot

The Return of The Spot

by *Gez Walsh*

The King's England Press

1997

The Return of The Spot is typeset in 14pt Baskerville and published by The King's England Press, Cambertown House, Commercial Road, Goldthorpe, Rotherham, South Yorkshire, S63 9BL.

ISBN 1 872438 19 9

Sixth Impression, 2001
Text and illustrations
© Gez Walsh 1997
The author asserts the moral right to be recognised as the author of this work for copyright purposes under the terms of the Berne Convention

Printed and bound in Great Britain by
Woolnough Bookbinding
Irthlingborough
Northamptonshire

FOREWORD

I never thought, in the many years I have been a publisher, that I would ever begin letters to potential customers with those immortal words "The Spot on My Bum". But then, I didn't know Gez Walsh.

The phenomenal success of his first book has been impossible to ignore, though there are those - such as the supermarket bookbuying executives working themselves into a lather over whether the word "bum" is offensive - who probably wish they could ignore it, if the public would only let them!

Gez Walsh is a writer you will either love or hate: if you don't like his writing, then, as authors used to say in the more genteel era of letters, Dear Reader, pass on. Gez has never claimed to be a literary genius. The story of how his first book, *The Spot on My Bum*, came to be written, to encourage his dyslexic son to read, is now probably almost too well known to need repeating.

Gez has that gift of catching the idiom of the everyday word, what Ian McMillan referred to in his foreword to the first book as "the voice of the playground, the voice of the top deck of the bus", and this new collection remains true to that style.

It is not to everyone's taste. Some people would prefer to pretend that snot, poops and farts do not exist, others find them subjects for exquisite and uproarious humour, especially children, who have always been more interested in forbidden subjects than in what they should be doing.

If there is one overriding thing which Gez has done for which he should be thanked and honoured, it is that, by writing about such subjects, he has brought in to the habit of appreciating poetry people who would probably never have dreamed of reading it. For that, even the most prudish of critics should forgive him his subject matter.

I have made this all sound very serious: in fact, what these books are, in mine and most people's opinions, is very, very, funny. Gez has added to the sum total of laughter in the world, which is also not a bad thing in itself.

So: whoever you are, and whatever age of childhood you have reached, loosen your stays and read on!

STEVE RUDD

To my grandad, James Walsh, who started the family tradition of telling silly stories and rhymes, and my father, Peter Walsh, who carried on the tradition. Finally, to Lee Walsh, who will tell them to future generations.

The Return of the Spot

Remember me,
I had a spot on my bum,
Which exploded one day
In the face of my mum.

Well my spot is back,
But just where do you suppose?
It's not on my bum,
It's on the end of my nose.

But this time it's bigger,
A real giant of a spot,
My nose is like a jelly
With a big custard top.

My friends no longer call,
Just to have a chat,
For fear my spot will pop
And in their faces go splat.

So it's up to the bathroom
To get rid of this spot,
I'll give it a squeeze,
And hope that it pops.

So I gave it a squeeze,
Which brought tears to my eyes,
Then my nose exploded,
Much to my surprise.

The bathroom mirror was covered
In a dripping yellow slop,
Like slippy, sloppy custard,
One hell of a pop.

So that is it,
Though my nose is still red.
My spot has now gone,
But there's a hole there instead.

The Classic Dancer

I will tell you a story,
But I'll tell it in rhyme,
It's about a party,
And having a good time.

It was grandma's party,
She was ninety years old,
She was sipping sherry
Like a merry old soul.

The music was playing,
It was very loud,
When I noticed a dancer
In the middle of a crowd.

He was just stood there,
With his arms in the air,
Waddling his bum
Like he hadn't a care.
He flapped his arms,
Just like a chicken,
He bobbed his head,
Then started clucking.
Cluck, cluck, cluck cluck cluck.

I said "Look here mum,
Look at this man.
Get over here,
As fast as you can."

We started laughing,
Saying he must be mad.
Then we let out a scream
When we realised it was dad.

He was just stood there,
With his arms in the air,
Waddling his bum
Like he hadn't a care.
He flapped his arms,
Just like a chicken.
He bobbed his head,
Then started clucking.
Cluck, cluck, cluck cluck cluck.

The music was loud,
Our ears were ringing.
There was worse to come,
Dad started singing.

He was telling people
He was Baby Spice,
You have never seen
Such a sight in your life.

He was just stood there,
With his arms in the air,
Waddling his bum
Like he hadn't a care.
He flapped his arms,
Just like a chicken.
He bobbed his head,
Then started clucking.
Cluck, cluck, cluck cluck cluck.

Then dad grabbed granny,
And swung her round.
Her teeth fell out,
Landing on the ground.

Mum gave dad
Such a smack,
Saying "Stupid fool,
She'll have a heart attack."

People were laughing,
It was so embarrassing,
But not for dad.
He just kept on dancing.

He was still stood there,
With his arms in the air,
Waddling his bum
Like he hadn't a care.

He flapped his arms,
Just like a chicken,
He bobbed his head,
Then started clucking.
Cluck, Cluck, cluck cluck cluck.

Poor old dad
Was fast losing pace,
His shirt wide open,
Sweat on his face.

His dancing's caused
By a drinking binge.
The stupid lump
Just made me cringe.

So if you think
That alcohol is cool,
Remember my dad,
That could be YOU!

Just stood there,
With your arms in the air,
Waddling your bum,
Like you haven't a care.
Flapping your arms,
Just like a chicken,
Bobbing your head,
Then starting clucking.
Cluck, cluck, cluck cluck cluck.

The Woman in Tweed

There was once a woman,
Who always wore tweed.
She thought it her job
To censor what children should read.
"You cannot read this,
You cannot read that",
She would say.
"Just read poems about fluffy cats."
Oh, what a silly woman,
Oh, what an awful pain.
All children are so different,
No two children are the same.
Some will like poems
About fluffy little cats,
Others love poems about
Horrible things like spots.
I will never write a poem
That this woman might like,
Because I'm a horrible child,
So she can get on her bike.
She can witter and rant,
Even get into a rage.
I will never write for her;
OI! WHAT'S THAT ON THE NEXT PAGE?

The Poem I Said I'd Never Write

Running through the town,
Climbing over walls.
Knocking over milk bottles,
Paying early morning calls.

Rummaging in dustbins,
Leaving your own scent.
Annoying all the pooches,
Having them barking at the fence.

Then when the sun rises,
And the world awakens for its work,
The cat snuggles up in its basket,
On its face a knowing smirk.

I'm Not Scared Of...?

I'm not scared of Dracula,
I'm not scared of Frankenstein,
I'm not scared of horror stories,
'Cos I'm not the scaring kind.

But just one thing,
Before you say goodnight,
Please don't leave me mum,
AND DON'T TURN OUT THE LIGHT!!

Mr...

I think my teacher's a fool,
I wish he didn't teach at my school.
He shouts and he rants,
Wears green flared pants,
And thinks mathematics is cool.

The Man from Amsterdam

There was once a man
From Amsterdam,
Who sailed the seas
Inside a pan.
It's not a very good
Sailing ship,
When you can't fit in
Past your hips.
And what a very strange
Place to live.
But it's better than
A rusty sieve.

What Am I?

I have no beginning,
I have no end.
I am always going
Around the bend.
I am always 'around'
But in different guises,
Always the same shape,
Just different sizes.
What am I?

Answer: a circle

19

Gnat Splat!

1, 2, 3, splat!
1, 2, 3, splat!
1, 2, 3, splat!
That's the sound
Of me swatting gnats
With my cricket bat.

The School Bully

The school bully is called Andrew,
And he thinks he's really tough.
He keeps on slapping my head,
He keeps on nicking my stuff.
But who cares what this creep says,
Because tonight he will pay
For all his evil ways.
When he puts on his wellies,
To rush home for his tea,
He will find them full of water;
Sorry, but I was dying for a wee!

The Million Heir

Dad walked in,
Shouting: "Gather round.
Pack your things, we're moving town.
We're moving up to the higher ranks,
Where windows have glass
And you keep your money in banks.

We no longer have to share
Just one bike,
We'll buy a car,
Do what we like.
No more holidays in the local park,
We'll go abroad, swim after dark."

So how had our fortunes turned around?
Had dad won one million pounds?
Dad said "No, but I will do soon,
I've bought a lottery ticket."
We all just sighed,
And left the room.

Look Mum!

Look mum, what do you think?
I've put a crocodile into the sink!
And if that doesn't make you laugh,
I've put a killer whale into the bath!

Animal Magic

The animals held a talent show,
At the local zoo.
There were lions and tigers,
Oh, and some pets had entered too.
The monkey started juggling,
Using rotten fruit,
The penguin sung an opera song,
In his opera suit.
The gorilla played a trick
On an unsuspecting crowd,
The hyena had a belly ache
From laughing far too loud.
"It's time to announce the winner,"
Said a grunting warthog.
"Please put your paws,
Hooves and claws together,
The winner is the dog."
The crowd they were delighted,
They roared "Take a bow."
The dog just looked puzzled,
Saying "Me bow, how?!

Oh, No!

Open the door,
The engines roar.
Miles below me
I see the floor.
The wind's in my face,
My heart starts to race.
Then I jump out of the 'plane.
From my face
The blood starts to drain,
When I realise I'm taking a direct route,
Because I've forgotten to pack my parachute.

Get Lost!!

If someone said
"Just get lost",
Would you growl,
Then get cross?
Or would you know
The way to go?
Wave goodbye,
And stamp on their toe!

I Can't Say This

I'm very sorry
About your yellow lorry.
I'm very sorry
About your red lorry, too.
But I can't say
Red lorry, yellow lorry,
Can you?

Hadrian's Wall

Once a Roman called Hadrian,
Built a very large wall.
He built it because he was sick and tired
Of the Picts paying him a call.
He built the wall from shore to shore,
The width of England wide,
Saying to the Celts "Just get lost,
And stick to your own blinking side."

Snakes

Mummy and baby snake
Were slithering through the grass.
Baby snake said "Mum, are we poisonous?"
His mum said "No, why do you ask?
And why do you look so worried
For one so very young?"
Baby said "I'm so glad to hear that,
Because I've gone and bitten my tongue."

I Didn't Cry

I trapped my finger
In the door.
It throbbed like mad,
It wasn't half sore.
But I didn't cry!
My mum she soaked it
In some cream,
My lips they trembled,
I let out a scream.
But I didn't cry!
Mum wrapped my finger up,
Took me to the doctor's
To get checked up.
But I didn't cry!
The doctor said
My cut was bad.
He sewed it up,
I was a good lad.
But I didn't cry!
My mum my lips
She gently kissed,
Saying how brave
To behave like this.
But I didn't cry!
I JUST HAD SOMETHING IN MY EYE!

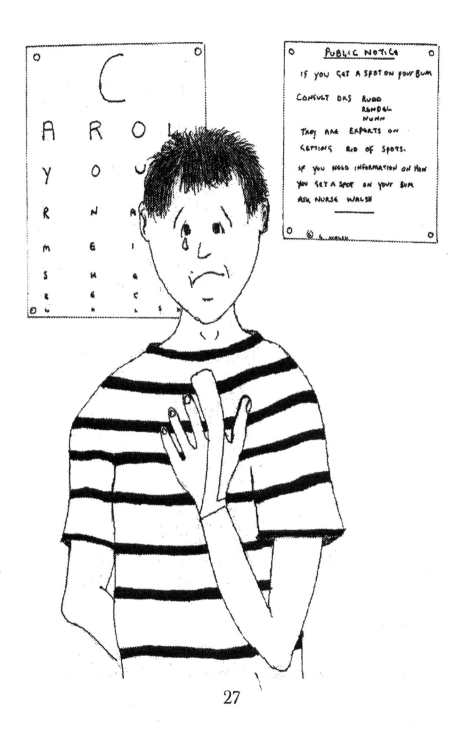

27

Don't Eat.....

Don't eat cowpats
For your breakfast,
Because people will think
That you use green tooth paste.
Don't eat toe nails
For your dinner,
Their lack of vitamins
Will make you thinner.
Don't eat maggots
For your tea,
Because with your stomach
They won't agree.
But you must eat beans
For your supper,
If you want to be
A super pooper!

Counting

One and one is two,
Two and two is four,
Three and three is six,
But I can't add up any more!

Hide and Seek

I always win
At hide and seek.
Others shut their eyes,
But I always take a peek.

The Island in the Air

There's an island in the air,
It must be way above my head.
My grandad told me about it,
"It's very beautiful", he said.
But my friends don't believe me,
I said "My grandad would never lie.
And last year grandad took grandma
On holiday to the Isle of Skye."

The Cheerleader

I'm a cheerleader
For a team called The Surry Nun.
I like cheering,
It's a lot of fun.
But because I'm dyslexic,
My spelling's not that good.
But this doesn't stop me,
I don't think that it should.
I just laugh
When I get things wrong.
This is what happened one day
While cheering the Surry Nun.
I shouted:
"Give me an 'S',
Give me an 'O',
Give me a 'G',
Give me a 'G',
Give me a 'Y',
Give me a 'B',
Give me a 'U',
Give me an 'M'.
And what have you got?
SOGGY BUM!

Counting Sheep

On a night I like to count sheep.
I do this every evening,
Before I go to sleep.
It was my brother who showed me how,
He said, "You must count sheep,
And not count cows."
So let me show you how it's done,
There are lots to count,
But I'll start with one.
I'd better say goodnight
Before I count my sheep,
Because when I get to ten
I'll be fast asleep!

Potty People

On a planet far away
Live the people of Potty,
Or so they say.
Now the people of Potty are different you see,
They like the opposite of you or me.
Just take for example
One of their marching songs.
Once you've heard it,
You'll know something's wrong.
"We're the people from Potty,
And we like our spotties,
Although they drive us potty.
They're all over our bodies,
From our noses to our botties.
We're covered in spotties,
So thanks a lotty."
So now you can see why they're called
The people of Potty.

The Rocking Vicar

Our vicar is such a shocker,
He's not like other vicars
Because he's a greasy rocker.
Yes, he thinks he's Elvis,
He curls his lip.
When he delivers his sermons
He shakes his hips.
He's got the power of love,
He's all shook up.
When asked a question
He says "Uh, uh."
An old lady once asked,
"What have you been doing today?"
The vicar picked up his guitar,
And started to play.
He curled his lip,
Then started to wail,
"I've been to a party at the county jail."
The old lady replied,
"Oh, that's very nice,
But you've said that before,
Maybe once or twice."
People just tut, saying
"A vicar in leathers and side burns
Looks so sad."
But for me it's worse,
Because the vicar's my dad!

Don't Go with Strangers

Don't go with strangers,
No matter what they say.
Don't go with anyone
Unless mum and dad say okay.
Don't go with strangers,
Not even for a walk down the lane,
Because if they take you by the hand
You may never see home again.

The King of Snow

A long time ago,
In a far away land,
Lived the King of Snow,
Who ruled with an iron hand.
The subjects of this king
Were industrious little elves,
Who gave the king all they made,
Leaving nothing for themselves.
But the Snow King wasn't happy,
He always wanted more,
So the elves they worked day and night,
Until they collapsed upon the floor.
So let this be a lesson,
Pay heed of this yourselves,
And always remember that
SNOWKING IS BAD FOR YOUR ELF!

I Feel So Bad

I can't stop crying,
I feel so bad,
It happened so quickly,
It's about my grandad.
It happened today,
About half past one.
I arrived home and
Dad said "I'm afraid grandad's gone."
Tears filled up in my eyes,
Dad gave me a hug.
I started to cry.
One minute he was sat
Just having fun,
The next he was laid out,
Mouth wide open and numb.
Now that it's over,
I hope it was quick.
The thought of him in pain
Makes me feel sick.
But my dad doesn't understand,
"Stop crying", he did shout.
"For heaven's sake, grandad's not dead,
He's only had his teeth out."

Alone in the Graveyard

*This poem should be told to your friends in a low
eerie voice. When you get to the last word, "You",
shout it out and watch them jump out of their skins.*

The wind was howling,
I was all alone.
It was late at night,
I couldn't find my way home.
I came to the graveyard,
I opened the gate.
My heart beat with such a rate.
As I walked among the grey headstones
I felt like crying,
I wanted to go home.
It was then that I heard it,
It was a ghostly sort of voice.
The chill of the wind
Made it an even more eerie noise.
The voice said,
"Are you scared?"
I stuttered "W-w-who?"
Then there was silence,
And the voice said
"**YOU!**"

I Like Grandma

I like my grandma
When she smiles.
She's got a big toothless grin,
Her mouth goes over her top lip
And her nose rests on her chin.

The Lumpy Bird

How absurd, the Lumpy bird.
If you make him jump,
He turns into a lump,
And lies on the floor
Like a turd.

Mrs. Clean

There was once a woman,
Her name was Jean,
She washed and scrubbed,
She was very, very clean.
Her house it sparkled
With such a sheen,
That when people passed
They shouted "Hi, Jean".

Barry is not Normal

Barry is not normal,
I think he comes from
Outer space,
Because his mum says
Any more cheek,
And he'll be laughing out of
The other side of his face.

Do I Look Like This?

Why is my head so small?
It's the size of a tennis ball.
The brains in me
Are the size of a pea,
And I know nothing at all.

Why is my belly so fat?
Why does it wobble like that?
I feed it so well,
So why does it swell,
And rest on my knees when I'm sat?

Why do I fart like a pig?
Why is my bum so big?
It must be three feet wide
From side to side,
And carried around in a rig.

Why are my legs so long?
Why do they give off such a pong?
They're hairy and thin,
Like two long pins,
And even my feet are wrong.

I think I look like this;
Mum says I'm a silly miss.
She says there's nothing wrong
With my head, legs, belly or bum,
Then she gives me a big hug and kiss.

Grandma's Snack

Last Sunday evening
My parents went out for tea.
They invited my gran round,
Just to sit in with me.

I like my gran,
She's so much fun,
She lets me do things
That would horrify my mum.

So when my parents
Were safely out of the way,
I asked my gran
"Could I bring my rabbit in to play?"

Gran thought for a moment,
Then she said "Yes,
But remember my girl,
You clean up any mess."

So I brought in Floppy,
And put her on the settee.
The first thing she did
Was to have a good pee.

Then she leaped into the air
And ran for the door,
Leaving lots of black droppings
All over the room floor.

So I caught hold of Floppy,
And put her back into her hutch.
I shook my finger at her
Saying "Well, thanks ever so much."

I sneaked into the kitchen
Where gran was cooking.
I pinched a paper bag
When she wasn't looking.

I went back into the room
To pick up the droppings.
I put them into the paper bag
Very quickly, without stopping.

It was then I had a 'phone call,
So I put the bag on the table,
And walked into the hall,
As fast as I was able.

It was my friend Jenny;
She'd 'phoned to tell me about her new pups,
But once she started talking
I just couldn't shut her up.

In the end I said,
"Look, Jenny, I really have to go."
So I put down the 'phone,
Then I turned and screamed "OH NO!"

You see gran didn't have her glasses,
And without them she cannot see.
She was eating out of the paper bag,
Saying "These raisins taste off to me."

Poor Little Deer

A poor little deer,
Born with no eyes,
Ran through the forest,
Always getting by.
But he didn't want pity,
He could look after himself.
Other deer admired him
For his strength and his stealth.
All problems he could overcome;
The first to sense danger,
The first on the run.
I was once asked his name
By a child keen to hear.
I just shrugged my shoulders
And said "No eyed deer."

The French Toilet

While on holiday
With my family in France,
I met a man,
Just by chance.
I was looking for the toilets,
I was by myself,
But I couldn't read the signs,
I needed some help.

I asked this man,
"Is this the toilet for me?"
He nodded his head,
Then he said "Oui."
I said "No I don't,
I want to pooh,
And I think you're so rude,
So what's it to you?"

Don't Exaggerate

I know a man so thin
He can slide down a grate.
No you don't, don't exaggerate.
Well, you know the Queen,
She's my best mate.
No she's not, don't exaggerate.
When I go fishing
I don't need any bait.
Yes you do, don't exaggerate.
I could eat a bun shop
Without putting on weight.
No you couldn't, don't exaggerate.
All girls love me,
I guess it must be fate.
Look, I've told you fifty million times,
DON'T EXAGGERATE!

Genie Lamp

I have found an oil lamp
Which has a genie inside.
I know he's in there,
No matter how he hides.
I've rubbed it, shaken it,
I've blown down the spout.
I threw it against the wall,
But that genie would not come out.

So I took off the top,
Just to have a look.
I know he's in there,
Because I read it in a book.
It said "Rub the lamp,
A genie will grant you three wishes."
And I need him to appear soon
So I don't have to wash up the dishes!

Call Me?

Give me a call,
Give me a ring,
Knock on my door,
Do just drop in.
So nice to see you,
How do you do?
Oi, what do *you* want?
I wasn't talking to *you*!

Kissing

I saw mum
Kissing dad.
I think it's disgusting,
I think they're sad.
Two grown ups,
Kissing each other.
I had to cover the eyes
Of my little brother.
I told mum,
Just what I think,
Letting herself go
By the kitchen sink.
It starts here,
But where will it end?
How would she feel
If I told all her friends?
Two old people,
Kissing like that,
In front of children,
And frightening the cat.
This must stop,
Just give it a rest.
Next she'll be going out
Without wearing her vest.
I think kissing's alright,
As long as you're young,
But my dad's thirty five,
And so is my mum!

Yup!

I met a cowboy
Who was carrying a pup.
I said "He's cute",
The cowboy said "Yup."
I said "Here's some water,
Would he like a sup?"
The cowboy smiled,
Then said "Yup."
I asked the cowboy
"Could I cuddle your pup?"
He nodded his head,
Then said "Yup."
He walked to his horse,
And saddled up.
I asked "Are you going now?"
The cowboy said "Yup."
He then climbed on his horse,
So I passed him his pup.
I said "Can I ask you a question?"
The cowboy said "Yup."
"Well, whatever I ask,
You just say 'yup'.
Can you say anything else?"
The cowboy said "Yup."
He'd done it again.
I was now fed up,

So I waved him goodbye,
And wished him good luck.
He took hold of the reins
And shouted "Giddy yup"!

The Wreck

There was once a ship
Which sailed the seven seas,
That boasted to the other ships
"I'm so fine, no-one's finer than me."
It said "Just look at my mast,
And my wonderful, painted bow.
I ferry the rich,
You ferry the cows."
Then one day, during a terrible storm,
The ship was abandoned,
And left lonely and forlorn.
Its mast had broken,
Crashing through the deck.
It was left dirty and scruffy,
It looked such a wreck.
Water was now seeping in
Through a hole in its side.
Then, without warning,
Under the sea it silently did slide.
It came to a halt
At the bottom of the sea.
No more passing ships
To call out "Hey, look at me."
It laid all alone,
Down in the deep.
Shaking with fear,

It started to weep.
The sharks swam around it,
Taking a long look.
The ship, full of fear,
Just shook and shook.
Then a shark burst out laughing
As it swam past the deck.
It shouted to its friends
"Hey, look at this, it's a NERVOUS WRECK!"

Why?

Why do people go to war?
Why are there rich?
Why are there poor?
Why do people sleep on the streets?
Why do children starve?
Why do I have so much to eat?
Why do adults think they know best?
Why don't they understand?
Why do they create such a mess?
Why do I watch the news,
With a tear in my eye?
Why don't you understand
Why I will always say "Why?"

You Can't Beat It

Mum was taken aback.
She said "Do that again
And I'll give you a smack."
She said "What a disgusting trick."
Just watching makes her feel sick.
But I say you can't beat it;
I love to pick my nose and eat it!

What is Puberty?

Mum said "It's time we talked
About the facts of life and puberty."
Then she waffled on about the birds and bees.
I said "Look, I don't like honey,
Or whistle in trees,
And I don't know what you're on about,
What the heck has this to do with me?"

Something Nasty in the Fridge

There is something nasty in our fridge,
It has escaped from a yogurt pot
By building a bridge.
The yogurt was nine months old,
When this furry creature crawled out,
Covered in slime and mould.
It is now running amok,
It's just doing as it pleases;
It's wrecked the Dairy Box
And eaten all the cheeses.
It's eaten a left-over curry,
And a cheese-cake as well,
It's taken over the fridge
And there's one heck of a smell.
So it was up to my mum,
With her bleach and a duster.
No-one messes with her,
She's a fungus buster.
So they did battle,
What a terrible sight.
But that mouldy old yogurt slob
Succumbed to mum's might.
So our fridge is now safe,
It's so spotless and clean.
But there could be trouble ahead,
Because there's a mouldy old tomato
That my mum hasn't seen.

Nitty Nora

At school today
We had a visitor;
It was Nitty Nora,
The hair inquisitor.
She searched through my hair,
On the sides
And down the back.
She found a white thing,
Gave it a squeeze
To see if it cracked.
Then she gave me a smile,
She looked thrilled to bits,
And said "I'm pleased to tell you
That you don't have nits!"

Carrots

Mum says if I eat carrots
I will be able to see at night.
But I'm not eating carrots,
And if I want to see in the dark
I'll just turn on the light.

Oops!!

Well, knock me down
And slap my thighs,
Just tickle my head,
But cover your eyes.
I am very worried
There's something wrong:
It's me to blame
For this terrible pong!
Oh mum and dad, I'm not very happy,
'Cos I've done a bottom burp
And filled my nappy.

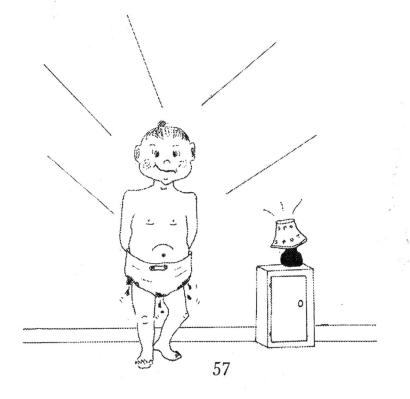

Mis-spelling

(This poem should be sung to the Christmas carol Noel)

One Christmas time,
Santa sent a card
To his favourite reindeer,
Who always worked so hard.
It said "To my friend Rudoph,
The red-nosed reindeer."
Rudolph said "That's nice,
But you've spelled my name wrong I fear."
The elves they laughed,
Then they started to sing:
"Santa you're a good man,
But terrible at spelling.
There's no 'L' no 'L', no 'L' no 'L'!

At What Time?

At what time should you go to the dentist?
What time is it right for you?
Is the right time when you need a check-up?
Would you be scared, would you see it through?
Always make sure your mouth's clean, not dirty,
Because the wrong time to go to the dentist,
Is when you let it get to TOOTH HURTY.

The Man with the Knife

The man was in the living room,
With a big knife in his hand.
The children were in the kitchen,
Trying to work out a plan.
The man walked through the hall-way,
With the big knife still in his hand.
The children were all hidden,
Trying not to make a sound.
The man with the knife,
He smiled through gritted teeth,
Then walked over to the table
Which the children had hidden beneath.
The man looked under the table,
The children all went mad,
Shouting "We thought you'd never find us.
Are you cooking supper for us dad?"

The Healthy Spud

Why not try a healthy spud,
It's much better than a greasy pud.
Go on, try it, but please don't fry it,
As too much grease won't do you any good.
You can bake it, boil it,
Even roasting it won't spoil it.
Wash it, mash it,
Cook it in its jacket.
Why not try it,
Just a few times a week?
Oh yes, if you just add veg
You get a bubble and squeak.

Harold and William

Once upon a time a young boy,
Who's name was Harold English,
Lived on Hastings Road,
At number 1066.
Now Harold was a bully,
And thought that he was king.
He picked on all the young kids,
And most were scared of him.

But Harold's days were numbered
As the local bully king,
Because down the road at number twenty four,
A boy named William French moved in.
William was also a bully,
Who loved to hit kids with conkers.
He always carried some around with him,
So he was known as William The Conker.

Then one fateful day
The two bullies met head on.
They both knew that they had to sort it,
Because with bully kings there must be just one.
Both lads stood their ground,
Both were in 'destroy' mode.
All the other kids ran and hid
To watch the Battle of Hastings Road.

So the battle began,
But I'm afraid Harold had met his match.
William had the upper hand,
Pushing Harold into Mr. Jones' vegetable patch.
William looked around
And found a marrow nearby.
He quickly picked it up and threw it,
Hitting Harold in the left eye.
Harold could not take it,
He soon started to cry,
Saying "Why did you do that?
I've got a marrow in my eye."
And so the battle was over,
The winner was William The Conker.
Harold is never seen any more.
Now William is the king bully plonker.

I Don't Have a Problem With.....

I don't have a problem wiv you,

And I don't have a problem wiv Jim.

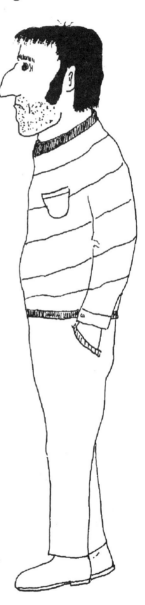

I don't have a problem wiv Mary,

BUT I'VE GOT A PROBLEM WIV HIM!

My First Kiss

I remember my first kiss,
It was with Sharon Lear:
My heart, it started racing,
And I was gripped with fear.
The way she smiled
It just melted my heart;
I tried to look cool,
While just falling apart.
Her lips they drew close,
My body went numb,
I'd never kissed a girl before:
Well, only my Mum.
I remember the moment
Our teeth banged together,
I knew she was for me,
I would love her forever.
But that was so long ago,
Now we don't even speak.
To me it was like yesterday,
I can't believe it was last week!

Poorly Julie

Poorly Julie
Lay on her bed,
Spots on her body,
Pain in her head.
Her mother called the doctor,
Who arrived a little late.
He just shook his head, saying
"It's something you ate."
Julie said "I don't believe it, never, no way,
I've just eaten the same
As I do each day.
That's 4lbs of chocolate,
26 bags of crisps,
3 large cakes,
Oh, and 20 candy sticks."
Then Julie smiled,
"I know what's causing these spots,
It's that sprig of broccoli I ate
At Auntie Dot's."

The Race

I've got to start running,
I've got to run fast.
But I don't know who I'm racing,
I don't know who to pass.
It was my teacher who told me:
"Stop sitting and staring into space",
And it was time that I grew up,
And joined the human race.

The Poem Without Rude Words

I am writing this poem,
Although it breaks my heart.
Mums and teachers have told me
That I can no longer say 'fart'.
I can't say 'bum' or 'spot',
I can't mention 'willies',
Or noses full of 'snot'.
The teachers said that I was far too crude,
And the children shouldn't hear words so rude.
So in this poem I won't say
'Fart', 'bum' or 'spot',
And clever poets
Don't need noses full of 'snot'.
So for mums and teachers
I will just take a deep breath:
Fart
Bum
Willy
Spot
Snot
There, I bet that scared you to death!

Pirates

There was once a bunch of pirates,
Who sailed the seven seas.
They were not very good at pirating,
And they ate jelly for their tea.
The leader of this motley bunch
Was a man that no-one feared.
His biggest disappointment in life
Was that he could not grow a beard.
So to hide the fact
His facial hair was very thin,
He bought himself a hamster,
And glued it to his chin.
The rest of the crew laughed
As the captain strolled around the deck,
Shouting "Ouch! Ooh! Ahh!"
As the hamster bit and scratched his neck.
The rest of the crew
Were just as strange as the captain.
All were very daft,
All had only half a brain.
There was Peg Leg Sam,
Who had legs like pegs,
And a face as pink as spam.
Shirley Shout, who screamed at people
As she walked about.
The next one up
Is No You Can't Tim,

Who was tall and thin,
And would not let people do anything.
And last and least
Was a strange looking beast
Called Fred The Bore:
As soon as he spoke,
People started to snore.
He had a big, fat belly
And a very shiny head.
When he spoke, people would say
"Oh, drop dead Fred!"
Then one day Peg Leg Sam
Grew fed up of his lot.
"We never steal any treasure", he said,
"And as for eating jelly,
Well it just brings me out in spots."
So he organised a mutiny,
But no-one walked the plank.
The captain he just resigned
And got a job in a well-known bank.
The rest of the crew,
Sick of looking such fools,
They all got jobs as teachers;
Have you seen them working in your school?

The Monster Party

The monsters had a party,
Everyone was there,
From Frankenstein to Dracula, and the Gorgons
Who have snakes instead of hair.

The skeletons looked nervous,
They shook their rickety bones,
Because they knew a Gorgon stare
Could turn them all to stone.

The Mummy had a dance,
Shaking off pieces of his body.
Frankenstein just laughed,
Saying "Isn't Egyptian workmanship shoddy!

The Blob squelched
As he moved around the room.
He bumped into the Wolfman,
Who was howling at the moon.

The Wolfman growled
As the Blob slithered over his toes,
Then he jumped upon the Blob,
And bit him on the nose.

Dracula shouted "Stop!
Everyone please be good.
Now come and have a drink with me,
Mine's a pint of blood."

So on went the party,
They sang and danced throughout the night.
The Mummy shook his head off,
Which gave him such a fright.

Soon it was morning,
They heard the cockerel call,
So they all ran back to their graves
Until next week, when it's the Banshee's ball.

Bubble Bath

Our neighbours have a jacuzzi;
It's a bath that blows out bubbles.
They say it cost a lot of money
And to fit it was such trouble.
My brother and I thought it strange,
In fact we had to laugh.
We've had our own jacuzzi for years,
Just by farting in the bath!

Up My Nose

I had to go to hospital,
You'll want to know why I suppose.
Well, it's because Daniel Higgins
Shoved a dried pea up my nose.
At first I thought it funny,
Having a pea up my snout.
But I soon stopped laughing
When I realised it wouldn't come out.
I prodded and poked it
With my finger tip,
But the more I poked,
The further it went up.
Then I tried to blow it out,
But this just made me dizzy,
So I went to tell my teacher
Who said "Not now Wilf, I'm busy."
The children in my class
Asked if they could have a look.
Some tried to poke it out with pencils,
I was even hit on the head with a book.
Soon my teacher noticed
That something was wrong,
Shouting "Kirsty, take that pen out of Wilf's nose
What the heck is going on?"
So, after telling teacher the story,
Of how the pea got up my snout,

She took me to the hospital
To have it pulled back out.
The nurse took me into a room,
And laid me on a bed.
She shone a torch up my nose,
And looked deep into my head.
Then, taking some long pliers,
She shoved them up my nose.
I screamed, "Watch my eyeball!"
As I curled up my toes.
"Ah, there it is", said the Nurse,
Holding it out for all to see.
On the end of the long pliers
Was a snotty green pea.
So now I've learned my lesson,
My nose is now a pea-free zone,
And if Daniel wants to shove a pea up a nose,
He can blinking well use his own!

Claptrap

Claire Clarke
Called Clarence Clone
A clacking clown.
Clarence Clone
Clipped Claire Clarke's curls
Calling clever Claire Clarke
Curly claptrap.

Senseless

I watched a film about an elephant,
That had a small child.
These two majestic beasts
Walked proudly in the wild.
The mother was so huge,
And had no fears as such.
The little one ran around,
Comforted by the mother's gentle touch.
All the other animals
Gave the elephant respect.
They would not attack,
Because they knew what to expect.
But there was just one animal
That could kill this gentle beast,
But unlike other animals
On its flesh it would not feast.
So this gentle mother,
Walking proudly with her son,
Was one day ambushed, killed,
Her body left to rot
In the blazing, midday sun.
So the little one was orphaned,
Left all alone to die;
He ran around his mother's corpse
With tears in his eyes.
Why had the mother died?

Well, she had extra-long tusks,
Which were ripped from her head,
Leaving a rotting husk.
Oh yes; the name of this animal,
Who kills because it can,
Is supposed to be the most intelligent:
The animal's name is MAN!

Author's Postcript

Just when you thought it was safe to go back in the bookshops, along comes Spot II, The Return of ... more childish rudeness, written by an idiot.

This is a collection of old jokes put into rhyme, new jokes put into rhyme, poems you can sing, poems you can dance to, poems to make you think: oh, yes, and there are also some about farting, snot and spots.

This book, just like my last book, *The Spot on My Bum*, is all about encouraging children to pick up a book and read. It is written in a basic style with playground humour, for children from seven to seventy to have a laugh. Some people do not agree with the subject matter which I use to encourage children to read and write, saying it is too crude. Personally I would rather have a child try to spell the word "fart" than not try to spell at all. So, if this book is not to your taste - stop eating it!

Gez Walsh

Acknowledgements

Thanks to Steve Rudd and Debbie Nunn for all their hard work in sorting out my gaffes. Also thanks to Phil Rendell for helping *The Spot* to become such a success and for all the lifts. And thanks to all the people who bought my first book, and to Terry Sorfleet for continuing to believe in it all.

Thanks to Carol and Lee for putting up with me.

Last but not least, thanks to my brother John for his support and encouragement, and for being a friend.